Twenty
Names In
SPORT

Toni Williamson

Illustrated by Gary Rees

MARSHALL CAVENDISH
New York, London, Toronto

Editor: Rosemary Ashley
Consultant Editor: Maggi McCormick

Reference Edition published 1988

© Marshall Cavendish Limited 1988
© Wayland (Publishers) Limited 1988

Published by Marshall Cavendish Corporation
147 West Merrick Road
Freeport
Long Island
N.Y. 11520

Library of Congress Cataloging in Publication Data

Williamson, Toni.
    Twenty names in sport / Toni Williamson.
        p. cm. — (Twenty names)
    Bibliography: p.
    Includes index.
    Summary: A collection of twenty brief biographies of sports figures.
    ISBN 0-86307-969-7 : $12.95
    1. Athletes-Biography-Juvenile literature. [1. Athletes.
2. Sports-Biography.] I. Title. II. Title: 20 names in sport.
III. SedieGV697, A1W54 1988
796' .092'2-dc19
[B]   88-20994
                                              CIP
                                               AC

Printed in Italy by G. Canale & C. S.p.A. - Turin.

Contents

The will to win

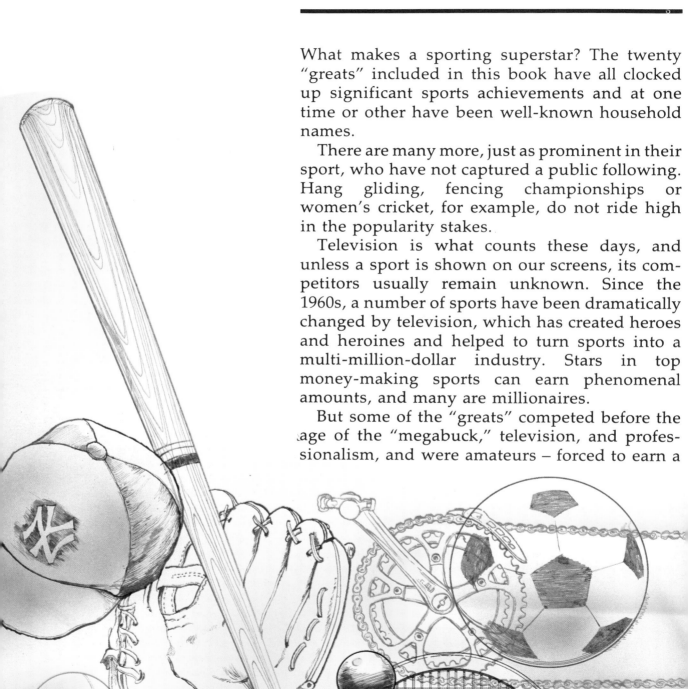

What makes a sporting superstar? The twenty "greats" included in this book have all clocked up significant sports achievements and at one time or other have been well-known household names.

There are many more, just as prominent in their sport, who have not captured a public following. Hang gliding, fencing championships or women's cricket, for example, do not ride high in the popularity stakes.

Television is what counts these days, and unless a sport is shown on our screens, its competitors usually remain unknown. Since the 1960s, a number of sports have been dramatically changed by television, which has created heroes and heroines and helped to turn sports into a multi-million-dollar industry. Stars in top money-making sports can earn phenomenal amounts, and many are millionaires.

But some of the "greats" competed before the age of the "megabuck," television, and professionalism, and were amateurs – forced to earn a living, as well as train in their particular sport. Their names live on because their achievements were so spectacular.

To reach the peak of any sport is hard. It requires full-time training, single-minded dedication, an overwhelming to win and, if the following "names" are typical examples, a strong personality is also needed.

The women in this book are particularly outspoken – and sports could do with more like them. Despite women's tennis, many sportswomen are still fighting for equal acceptance in what is essentially a male world.

But both men and women are inevitably drawn into political controversies, tragedies, and gestures that take place in the sporting arena. Unfortunately, there is no space in this book to give accounts of the massacre of eleven Israelis at the Munich Olympics, national boycotts of major events, or to explain the exclusion of South Africa from virtually all international competition. But you may want to consider these aspects as you read the following pages.

1
Babe Ruth

Babe Ruth towered over his age in more ways than one. He was a giant, both in physique and performance, and at the plate, he wielded a bat weighing a third heavier than any other player could swing.

When he played for the Boston Red Sox, he was known as a pitcher; but, after he joined the New York Yankees, he developed as a batsman. He was the hardest hitter baseball had known and was nicknamed "King of Swat." At his peak, almost every ball he hit sailed over the stands – and the crowd loved it.

Babe Ruth's was a "rags to riches" story in the best American tradition. At the age of seven, he was sent to a Baltimore orphanage and reform school where he was said to be "incorrigible." He lived there most of the time until he was signed up by the Baltimore Orioles at the age of nineteen.

Below *Babe Ruth, the hard-hitting giant with the heavy bat, sends the ball soaring high over the stands.*

During the 1920s, sports stars were treated like Hollywood movie stars. Ruth was mobbed wherever he went, but the popularity and glamour went to his head, and he was frequently in trouble with the authorities. He was once described as a glutton, a drunkard, and a hell raiser, but he was loved by all, because of his casual, generous personality.

He also had a reputation as a womanizer, but he was no beauty. His weight ballooned during his career, and he had a massive paunch. He seldom weighed below 220 pounds, and sometimes the scales went as high as 270.

Babe Ruth ended his career on a sad, defeated note. His performance showed the effects of too many years of alcohol, a huge appetite, and too many late nights. He hoped for a job as baseball manager, but the offer never came.

America's greatest sports hero made his last appearance at Yankee Stadium on its 25th anniversary, eight weeks before his death. Ruth was dying of cancer, and the crowds gave him his last tumultuous ovation.

Above *Baseball's legendary hero waves to cheering crowds at Yankee Stadium in 1948.*

1895	born in Baltimore
1902	sent to training and reform school
1914	leaves reform school and joins Boston Orioles
1914	signs up with Boston Red Sox
1919	breaks home run record of 29 with 54 in one season
1920	signs with New York Yankees
1921	makes 59 home runs
1935	retires from baseball
1947	sets up the Babe Ruth Foundation to help underprivileged children
1948	appears at Yankee Stadium on its anniversary, dies of cancer 8 weeks later

2
Johnny Weissmuller

Next time an old Tarzan movie is shown on television, observe the hero's front crawl technique as he swims fearlessly through crocodile-infested waters! It is very likely that the muscular jungle star, with his piercing jungle call, will be Johnny Weissmuller – the most famous of all Tarzans and a sensational Olympic swimmer.

Although frail as a youngster, Johnny grew to over 6 feet and developed an impressive physique. He broke his first world record at seventeen and went on to break twenty-three more during his competitive career.

He also collected fifty-two US titles and five Olympic gold medals at two Games, and he was the first man to break the minute record for 100m and five minute record for 400m freestyle. His most impressive record was 51.00 seconds for 100yd freestyle, which was undefeated for ten years.

Below *Weissmuller, the original hero of the Tarzan films. (Right) he won five gold medals at the 1924 Olympics in Paris.*

Weissmuller's revolutionary high-riding stroke action had a lasting impact on the development of the front crawl, and, in 1950, he was voted greatest swimmer of the half century by American sportswriters.

Weissmuller turned professional in 1929, appearing in swimming exhibitions. But, on the promise of a free lunch with movie star Greta Garbo (or so the story goes), he agreed to take a test for the screen's first talking Tarzan. He beat 150 other Tarzans hopefuls for the part and starred in a dozen movies. But he still kept superbly fit and set a personal best time of 48.5 seconds for 100yd freestyle when he was thirty-six years old.

He soon took to Hollywood life, earning a fortune and marrying six times. By 1948, age and weight were creeping up on him, but he was offered the part of Jungle Jim in a series of feature films which led to a television series. When the series ended, he took charge of the Swimming Hall of Fame in Florida until he suffered a stroke in 1977.

Above *Weissmuller and actress Maureen O'Sullivan as Tarzan and Jane.*

1904 born in US
1922 sets his first world record, aged 17
1924 Paris Olympics: wins three gold medals – 100m and 200m freestyle and 200m freestyle relay: bronze medal for water polo
1927 sets world record of 51.00sec for 100yd
1928 Amsterdam Olympics: wins two gold medals – 100m freestyle and 200m relay
1932 makes his first Tarzan movie: *Tarzan, the Ape Man*
1948–55 stars in *Jungle Jim* movies, followed in 1956 by a TV series
1984 dies in Mexico

3
Juan Fangio

"The Fangio Year" was 1957, only a year before the Argentinian Juan Fangio retired from motor racing. His younger rivals nicknamed him "old man," but he was at his absolute peak and then, as now, he was considered the world's number one racing driver.

Fangio was one of the first to sit behind the wheel of the then revolutionary streamlined cars, and he combined fast driving with immaculate car control and a relaxed, calm driving style.

Because of World War II (1939–45), he did not enter a European Grand Prix until he was thirty-seven, but during the following ten years, he became world champion five times.

Fangio helped in a garage as a small boy and later worked as a mechanic, building his own racing cars at night. His favorite race during the early days was the Gran Premio Nacional, a

1911 born in Argentina
1940 first great victory – Gran Premio Internacional del Norte, in South America
1949 first European victory at San Remo Grand Prix
1951 wins World Championship
1951 accident in Monza Grand Prix
1954–7 world champion four years in succession
1958 kidnapped in Cuba and later released
1958 retires

grueling long-distance event over thousands of miles in South America, through jungle and over mountains.

Racing drivers dice with death. During a 24-hour Le Mans race, Fangio narrowly skirted a crash which killed more than ninety spectators. But he did not always escape unscathed. After driving all night to Monza for a Grand Prix, he crashed during the race and was unconscious for days and in a cast for five months.

Fangio hit the headlines in a somewhat different story in 1958, when he was kidnapped by revolutionaries while visiting Cuba for a race (he was released safely after the event).

That same year, Fangio reckoned he had exhausted his store of good luck and retired from a sport which had killed many of his friends and rivals. He was not past his peak, but he had fulfilled his ambitions. For such a champion, a sixth world title would have meant little.

Above *Fangio and his wife at Silverstone Circuit in England in 1954.*

Below *Fangio, the world's number-one racing driver in the 1950s, once again takes the winner's checkered flag.*

4

Mildred "Babe" Didrikson

1911	born in US
1930	leaves school to play semi-professional basketball with Golden Cyclones in Dallas
1930–2	All-American basketball player
1932	enters national women's team athletics championship, competes in several events and wins title
1932	Los Angeles Olympics: she wins six gold medals and breaks four world records within three hours
1938	marries George Zaharias, wrestler
1943	wins 17 golf tournaments in a row and is first American to win the British Ladies Amateur (Golf) Championship
1950	voted Woman Athlete of the Half Century
1954	wins US Women's Open by a record 12 strokes only 15 months after major surgery for cancer
1956	dies of cancer

"Whatta-Gal!" That's what the press called Didrikson in her heyday. Otherwise, the woman who was considered the greatest female athlete of all time was known as Babe, after baseballer Babe Ruth.

Whatever sport Babe tried, she was an instant phenomenon. She was an All-American basketball player and played excellent baseball and softball. She won tennis tournaments, diving championships, and could swim close to world record times. Only three months after being shown the javelin, shot putt, high jump, long jump, and baseball throw, she held national records in two of the events. Within nineteen months, she was recognized as a world class athlete.

But Babe came from a poor, unsophisticated background, and her fellow competitors believed success had gone to her head. They thought she was arrogant because she bragged about her sporting ability. But Babe was like that. She had never been quiet or ladylike and was always laughing and entertaining everyone with her harmonica.

After her success at the 1932 Olympics, Babe earned her living like Jesse Owens, by giving exhibitions. Then she took up golf, which brought her even more fame and fortune – and was considered a more acceptable sport for women.

There were not many professional golf championships for women in the 1930s, so Babe's success was hampered at first. But after the war, the situation improved. Babe helped set up the women's professional golf circuit, which she dominated with her powerful game.

In 1953, it was discovered she had cancer. The following year, after an operation and still suffering from cancer, she won five golf tournaments including the prestigious US Open. Two years later, only forty-five years old, she died.

Below *Mildred "Babe" Didrickson (right and inset) won the 80m women's hurdles and the women's javelin at the 1932 Olympic Games.*

5
Jesse Owens

On May 25, 1935, Jesse Owens performed athletics' greatest feat: he set six world records within 45 minutes. At the Berlin Olympics the following year, this sprinter, long jumper, and low hurdler confirmed his greatness by winning four gold medals and equaling or breaking twelve Olympic records.

Owens was born into poverty. He was the youngest of ten children, and the family lived in a cramped shanty in Alabama. After the First World War, they moved north to Cleveland. The family were still poor, but Owens was sent to a school where his athletic talents were recognized and developed. His outstanding athletic abilities soon made him a local hero and helped him win a place at Ohio State University and a place on the US Olympic team.

There were nineteen black athletes chosen to represent the US in Berlin in 1936 – more than ever before. Yet the Olympic opening ceremony was a showpiece for the Nazi party, and Hitler

1913 born in Alabama
1934 first world record: indoor long jump
1935 competes for Ohio State University in Western Athletics Championships and breaks 6 world records
1936 Berlin Olympics: 4 gold medals – for 100m, 200m, long jump and sprint relay
1950 voted Greatest Track Athlete of the half century
1960 his last Olympic record broken
1980 dies of lung cancer

intended to the use the Games as proof for his theory of white Aryan supremacy.

Owens, of course, shattered Hitler's fascist dreams, and there is a much repeated story that the athlete was snubbed by the German leader because he was black. But it is also worth remembering that Owens returned home to a country which was itself still full of racial inequalities.

He received hundreds of lucrative offers after his Olympic success, and, because he wanted financial security, Owens turned professional. As a result, he was suspended from amateur athletics, and when the money-making offers came to nothing, he was forced to appear in exhibition races and compete against horses in spectacular stunts.

In the 1950s, Owens was taken up by politicians because he was deeply traditional and patriotic and, as a modern American hero, could appeal to people of all races. But he was unable to understand the changing attitudes of the 1960s, and he died in 1980, a disillusioned man.

Above *Owen's achievements shattered Hitler's dreams of an all-German victory at the Berlin Olympics in 1936.*

Left *Jesse Owens won four gold medals and dominated the Berlin Olympics.*

15

6
Tenzing Norgay

Mount Everest in the Himalayas is the highest mountain in the world at 29,028 feet. Despite several attempts, it remained unconquered until Tenzing and New Zealander Edmund Hillary reached the summit on May 29, 1953.

Like all high mountains, the challenge of Everest means surviving grueling weather conditions, extreme physical and mental hardship, and danger. It is estimated that one in ten climbers on Himalayan expeditions will die.

Tenzing and Hillary were chosen to make the bid for the summit by John Hunt, the leader of the British expedition. There were twelve climbers backed by thirty-six high-altitude porters, who helped carry food and gear up to the nine camps on Everest. Tenzing was in charge of the porters, but, because he had been on numerous high-altitude expeditions, including six previous attempts on Everest, he was also a full climbing member.

Below *Mount Everest is conquered at last! Tenzing and Hillary reach the summit of the world's highest mountain.*

Tenzing was Nepalese, born into the Sherpa mountain tribe, and he lived in the high valleys close to the great Himalayan mountains. He came from a simple peasant family of thirteen children – he was the eleventh. He could not read or write, and, when he was young, he looked after the family yak herd in the high pastures, where the grass ended and the glaciers began. Here, he dreamed of climbing the high peaks. He left home at eighteen with the intention of joining mountaineering expeditions as a porter.

Once Everest was conquered, Tenzing became an immediate hero and legend, especially in Asian countries. The press wanted to know which climber had reached the summit first, but as far as Tenzing and Hillary were concerned, they both did because neither could have got there without the other.

Tenzing spent the rest of his life working as Chief Instructor at the Himalayan Mountaineering Institute in Darjeeling. He was the inspiration for many young Indian mountaineers, and his greatest aim was to raise the public image of the Sherpas from that of humble porters to accomplished mountain climbers in their own right.

Above *Tenzing and Hillary photographed after their successful ascent.*

1914	born in Nepal
1935	joins his 1st expedition to Everest
1936	makes his 2nd expedition; turned back because of too much snow in North Col
1938	3rd expedition; turned back at 27,100 ft, about 1,900 ft from summit
1947	4th expedition; turned back by bad weather
1952	5th expedition; forced back by wind, only 800 ft from summit
1952	6th expedition fails
1953	finally reaches summit of Everest with Edmund Hillary
1955	appointed head of Himalayan Institute of Mountaineering at Darjeeling
1980	dies at Darjeeling

7
Lester Piggott

It was always said Lester Pigott would never make it as a jockey because he was too tall and too heavy. But Piggott was fiercely determined. He rode his first winner at the age of twelve, and his riding career lasted thirty-eight years.

Piggott came from a family of British jockeys. His father was a top-class steeplechase and Grand National trainer; his grandfather rode three Grand National winners; and his mother won the Newmarket Town Plate – the only race in those days which allowed women riders.

In the early days of his career, Piggott was often criticized for pushing horses too hard and using the whip too severely. He was soon known for his fearless and reckless riding, and at eighteen, he was given a six-month ban for "dangerous and erratic riding" – one of the stiffest and most controversial sentences ever imposed on a jockey.

Below *Lester Piggott was Champion Jockey of the Year eleven times, and during his career rode more than 5,000 winners.*

Piggott was a quiet, reserved man, and he used his partial deafness as an excuse for not hearing people! But his deafness did not stop him from winning. He rode more than 5,000 winners, made a record twenty-nine Classic wins and was Champion Jockey of the year eleven times. As a result, he is thought to be worth £10 million. Stories are told about his legendary tightfistedness which Piggott treats as a personal joke – but he can be generous.

In order to succeed as a jockey, Piggott needed to overcome his physical disadvantages. His natural weight was about 147 pounds, but, by maintaining a strict diet, he managed to keep it down to 118 pounds – a good racing weight. And to compensate for his height – 5′8″ – he developed an unmistakable style. He rode with his behind stuck up in the air which made him look as if he was kneeling on the horse. Fortunately, he had perfect balance!

1935	born in England
1948	rides his first winner, aged 12
1954	youngest winner (18) of Epsom Derby on Never Say Die
1960	rides 170 winners and wins Champion Jockey title
1964–7	wins Champion Jockey title each year
1970	wins 2000 Guineas, King George VI, Queen Elizabeth Stakes, St. Leger and Derby on Nijinsky
1981	involved in riding accident and nearly loses an ear
1985	retires; completes a successful first year as a trainer
1987	successfully prosecuted for tax evasion

8

Garfield Sobers

Garfield (Gary) Sobers is considered by many cricketing experts to be the greatest all-rounder the sport has ever known. He was an outstanding batsman, as well as being a particularly fine fielder. As a bowler, he could was equally devastating, with his medium-fast pace, finger spin, and wrist spin bowling techniques.

There was always an expectant air among the spectators when Sobers, a left-hander, went to the crease or took up the bowling. He was extremely versatile, and during ninety-three test matches, he clocked up 8,032 runs, 235 wickets and 109 catches.

Sobers came from the Bay area of Barbados and spent his childhood playing knee or softball cricket. He was a cricket "natural," and in his third test, when he was twenty-one, Sobers not only made his first test century, but he continued to bat and break the world test score of 365 not out! He was one of the busiest, most popular, and best paid of professional cricketers – although he also played golf, soccer, and basketball for Barbados.

Until 1971, he was the undisputed number one player in the world. He produced exciting cricket – he was the only player ever to have hit six sixes in a six-ball over in a first class match – and his distinguishing trade mark, an up-turned shirt collar, became quite the fashion with admiring boys!

But Sobers made the mistake of playing in Rhodesia (now Zimbabwe), which was still under white minority rule and the outcry against him, especially in the West Indies, was fierce. His enthusiasam for cricket began to fade, and he was forced to retire sooner than intended because of an old knee injury.

Above and below *Gary Sobers was one of the world's greatest all-round cricketers. He was an outstanding batsman, brilliant fielder and devastating bowler.*

1935	born in Barbados
1954	first test match for West Indies against England at Jamaica
1958	first test century and world record of 365 not out against Pakistan at Sabina Park, Jamaica
1958	goes to England as a professional and begins playing in Lancashire League for Radcliffe
1965	appointed captain of West Indies
1968	hits six sixes in a six-ball over while playing for Nottinghamshire against Glamorgan
1970	plays in Rhodesia and retires four years later, aged 38
1975	knighted in Barbados

9
Dawn Fraser

As Dawn Fraser wrote in her autobiography, she was no Saint Joan in a swimsuit! Although she broke twenty-seven world records, won twenty-three national titles, and was the only swimmer ever to win the same Olympic title at three Games in succession, her career was marked by controversy and sparked off the biggest disputes in Australian sports history.

She was a tough, streetwise kid, and her swimming career never ran smoothly. At the age of fourteen, she was suspended for eighteen months by the Australian Amateur Swimming Union (AASU) because they ruled she was a member of a professional swimming club.

As she grew older and swam regularly for the Australian national team, she was labeled as an outspoken individualist and was accused of being a bad influence on the other swimmers. When she was dismissed from the team following her refusal to swim in the medley relay at the

1937	born in Australia
1956	breaks oldest record in swimming history, swims 100m in 64.5 sec
1956	Melbourne Olympics – wins two golds (including 100m freestyle title) and one silver medal
1958	Commonwealth Games, Cardiff, Wales – wins 2 gold and 2 silver medals
1960	Rome Olympics – wins second 100m title plus two silver medals
1962	Commonwealth Games, Perth, Australia – wins 4 gold medals
1962	first woman to break one minute record for 100m
1964	Tokyo Olympics – takes third 100m title plus one silver medal; banned by AASU for pranks during Olympics
1968	ban lifted but she retires from competitive swimming

Rome Olympics in 1960, questions were even asked about her in the Australian Parliament!

Fraser's personal life was not trouble-free, either. Her father died from cancer, and three years later, her mother was killed in a motor accident, in a car driven by Fraser, who chipped bones in her neck and had to wear a steel brace. Incredibly, a few months later, she was still able to retain her 100m title at the Tokyo Olympics in 1964.

Those Olympics proved to be a disaster. She marched in the opening ceremony against strict orders and was reprimanded for not wearing the Australian team swimsuit. On the last day of the Olympics, she was arrested for a prank that involved theft of a policeman's bike, a chase through the Japanese Emperor's garden, and a bid to swim the palace moat.

Dawn Fraser was banned by the AASU for ten years. After four years, the ban was lifted, but by then she had given up competitive swimming completely.

Above *Dawn Fraser won the gold medal for freestyle at three successive Olympics.*

Below *Dawn was an all-rounder of great talent – she won Australian titles in butterfly and medley events.*

10
Pelé

Pelé, real name Edson Arantes da Nascimento, was a prolific goal scorer, and it seems no words can describe the magic he wrought on the soccer field. Some just called him "God!"

In the 1,254 games played before he retired in 1974, Pelé scored 1,217 goals. He had grace and fluency and an incredible awareness of what was happening on the pitch. In 1961, he achieved what was called "the most beautiful goal ever scored," when he dribbled the ball past the entire opposition team and scored.

Young Edson did not have an easy start in life. His father, a professional soccer player for his hometown in Brazil, was paid a meager salary, and the family was very poor.

Below *Edson Arantes da Nascimento – otherwise know as Pelé – the world's greatest-ever soccer player, scored more goals than any other player in the history of soccer.*

Pelé kicked a ball as soon as he could walk and played for the juvenile team of his father's club until he was made an offer by Santos, the State champions in the Brazilian first division. He began playing for the first team in 1959, when he was sixteen years old, and less than a year later, he played for Brazil.

Pelé played in three World Cup tournaments. In 1958 in Sweden, at the age of seventeen, he startled the world with his youthful talent. Brazil's success that year was followed by another in 1962. But this time Pelé had to withdraw with a groin strain after only two matches.

The 1966 World Cup was a disaster for Brazil, and Pelé vowed never to play World Cup football again. Luckily for Brazil, he changed his mind and in 1970, at the peak of his career, he led Brazil to victory once again in Mexico.

Although Pelé's earning power was immense, his business ventures were not well-advised, and he was threatened with bankruptcy. After his retirement, he accepted a three year contract to play for the New York Cosmos, reputedly for $4.5 million. Pelé helped promote soccer in the US, and during his last season, the Cosmos won the North American Soccer League Championship.

Above *Pelé's skills helped Brazil to three World Cup victories.*

1940	born in Brazil
1956	joins Santos Football Club
1957	plays first game for Brazil
1958	Brazil wins World Cup in Sweden
1962	Brazil wins World Cup in Chile
1966	Brazil eliminated from World Cup in England before quarter-finals
1969	scores 1,000th goal
1970	Brazil wins World Cup in Mexico
1971	plays last game for Brazil
1974	retires and plays last game for Santos
1975	signs with New York Cosmos

11
Jack Nicklaus

The US professional golfer nicknamed the "Golden Bear" succeeded popular champion Arnold Palmer, who had turned golf into a major public spectacle. But Nicklaus did not share his fellow American's popularity. He was chubby, appeared in unflattering clothes, and had an unattractive crew cut. During play, he often disappointed crowds with his detachment and reserve.

But he managed to win over the fickle public with his play and pleased his admirers by losing weight, letting his hair grow, and showing some emotion on the golf course.

Nicklaus has won more major titles than any other golfer. At forty-six, he refuses to retire, and, in 1986, he stunned everyone by winning one of golf's most prestigious tournaments, the Masters.

Nicklaus started playing golf when he was ten years old. His father, a pharmacist, belonged to

Below *Jack Nicklaus has won more major golf championships than any other player.*

the local country club, but the Nicklaus family were considered to be fairly low down the social scale. This snobbishness acted as a challenge for Nicklaus, spurring him to work hard and excel at his sport.

Overwhelming talent and desire to win keep him playing, and as a golfer, he is a perfectionist. He uses his incredibly strong back and leg muscles to generate power, and he hits the ball in an extremely controlled fashion.

Golf has been paying massive rewards to its best players since the mid-1970s, and Nicklaus has earned millions of dollars. In later years, in addition to competing on the golf circuit, he has developed a new career. He designs, builds, and sometimes manages golf courses. One of his best known is the Muirfield Village course near his Ohio home. At present, the golf courses in his name number 76 – almost as many as his 89 major tournament victories.

Above *Nicklaus getting out of trouble in a sand trap.*

1940 & 1959/61 wins US
National Amateur
Championship
1963/71/73/75/80 wins US
Professional Golf
Association
Championship
1963/65/66/72/75/86 wins US
Masters Championship
1966/70/78 wins British Open
Championship
1962/67/72/80 wins US Open
Championship

12

Muhammad Ali

"I am the greatest" was Ali's favorite chant. And who could argue with the man who was three times heavyweight boxing champion of the world?

Ali was always a show-off. He bragged, boasted, and clowned around in the ring. At the 1960 Rome Olympics, the team called him "Big Mouth," but he proved he was the best by winning the gold medal – which he proudly wore. Years later, when a gang of white youths tried to take the medal from him, he reacted to their racism by throwing the medal in the Ohio River.

In 1964, few thought Cassius Clay, as he was then called, would beat Sonny Liston for the world heavyweight title. But Ali produced a winning combination of skill, strength, and psychological tactics. "Float like a butterfly! Sting like a bee!" was his motto. And he did.

Then he shocked the world by identifying publicly with the Black Muslims led by Malcolm

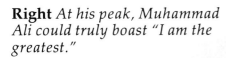

Right *At his peak, Muhammad Ali could truly boast "I am the greatest."*

X, the Black Separatist Leader. As a Muslim, Ali was a pacifist and refused to fight for the US in the Vietnam War (1959–73).

So, in 1968, he was stripped of his world title, which he had successfully defended nine times, and at his trial for draft evasion was fined and sentenced to five years in prison. He never went to jail, and the sentence was reversed in 1971, when public opinion was swinging against the war, but it could not make up for the three years he had been banned from the ring. He made an impressive comeback and regained the world title in 1974. He lost it in 1978, but then made history by winning for a third time in the same year.

Ali's last big fight and fourth attempt at the world throne was almost a farce. Age and too much time in the ring had finally caught up with him, and, for the first time in sixty professional fights, he was retired by the referee before the match had ended.

Above *Muhammad Ali retains his title against Richard Dunn in Munich in 1976.*

1942	born in US
1960	Rome Olympics – wins light-heavyweight gold medal
1964	wins first world heavyweight title, against Sonny Liston
1967	stripped of world title and banned from ring because of draft evasion
1971	loses to Joe Frazier in title fight
1974	regains title
1978	(February) loses title on points to Leon Spinks (September) wins it back from Spinks
1979	announces retirement
1980	loses to Larry Holmes in title fight

13
Jean Claude Killy

Below *Killy, the first ski superstar, retired at twenty-four after winning all the major skiing titles.*

Jean Claude Killy was the first of the ski superstars. He was so much better than everyone else in the sport, and accumulated so many impressive titles and classic wins – including the feared Hahnenkamm downhill (race) at Kitzbühel – that by the age of twenty-four, he had nothing left to prove in Alpine skiing; so he retired.

Brought up in France's famous ski resort, Val d'Isère, Killy competed for the French ski team for almost eight years. He accepted any challenge, unlike most of today's skiers who tend to specialize, and he was equally happy tackling slalom, downhill, and giant slalom.

Killy had exceptionally strong calves and ankles, and on the downhill, he kept his skis wide

apart which added stability. This has now become standard ski technique.

He had reached the top of his sport by 1966 and then, over the next three years, proved his utter supremacy by collecting race titles, the World Championships and the newly-formed World Cup – winning twelve of its seventeen races. At the 1968 Winter Olympics, Killy won three gold medals, despite accidentally scraping all the wax off his skis before the start of the downhill and racing the slalom in dense fog.

As a sport, skiing has expanded into a multi-million dollar business. Killy works in the ski industry, selling his well-known name and expertise. He made a brief comeback in 1973, for the fun of it, and showed that he was still a world-class skier.

Above *Killy won three gold medals at the Winter Olympics at Grenoble in 1968.*

1943	born in France
1965–7	wins Hahnenkamm race at Kitzbühel
1966	wins downhill and combined downhill-slalom title at Portillo World Championships
1967	wins first World Cup with the maximum number of points possible
1968	wins three gold medals at winter Olympics, Grenoble
1968	wins World Cup with 81-point lead
1974	retires from world skiing

31

14
Billie Jean King

In the 1960s and 70s, Billie Jean King was not only a champion on the tennis court, winning world titles in both singles and doubles matches, she was also an outspoken champion for women's rights in tennis.

She was ranked number one in the world five times and was in the top ten for seventeen years, but her passage to success was not easy. She was not popular, and fans thought she was too competitive. But it was a desire for perfection that made her demand so much from her game.

From the age of eleven, King had ambitions to be a world class tennis player. At first, she had the same trouble as Jack Nicklaus and was not considered "socially acceptable" at the local tennis club. Her father was a fireman, and her homemade outfit and cheap racquet did not make her popular. That was not her only problem. Physically, Billie Jean was not ideal for the game. She was short and stocky, with poor eyesight, a

1943 born in US
1961 wins her first Wimbledon title playing doubles with Karen Hantze
1966 wins her first singles Wimbledon title
1967/68/72/73/75 wins five more Wimbledon singles titles
1970 loses Wimbledon final in memorable game against Margaret Court, taking 2hr 27min, the longest ladies final in history of Wimbledon
1967/71/72/74 US Women's champion
1974 sets up the Women's Sports Foundation to increase opportunities of women and girls in sports participation.
1979 wins record 20th Wimbledon title while partnering Martina Navratilova in doubles
1983 beaten when almost 40 years old by Andrea Jaeger, 18, in Wimbledon semi-finals

weak chest, and knee trouble. But she had a powerful personality and compensated for her shortcomings with acrobatic athleticism.

Once King became part of the international circuit, she was furious to find that women were not awarded the same prize money as men. She acted as spokeswoman for the "Women's Lob," the movement for equal pay in tennis. In the early 1970s, she plotted rebellion against the men players who did not want women on the circuit – because they wanted all the prize money for themselves!

With the support of a few other players, King organized a sponsorship deal for women's tennis and set up a separate tournament. By publicly criticizing discrimination against women, she introduced a tough professionalism among women players.

When she took up the challenge to compete against Bobby Riggs, the 1939 men's Wimbledon champion, it was a much publicized event, and King felt the reputation of women's tennis was at stake. But she need not have worried. She beat him in straight sets.

Above *Billie Jean King returning the ball with a delicate backhand volley.*

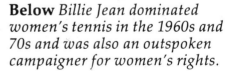

Below *Billie Jean dominated women's tennis in the 1960s and 70s and was also an outspoken campaigner for women's rights.*

15
Eddy Merckx

Eddie Merckx rode to greater heights of success and wealth than any other cyclist. His almost fanatical desire to win earned him the name "Cannibal," and his outstanding all-round ability as climber, sprinter, and time-trialist meant he set unbeatable standards in the cycling world.

Although Merckx had the sturdy build of a footballer instead of the usual light frame of a first-class cyclist, he was an exceptional rider. He was the first Belgian in thirty years to win the Tour de France, the grueling 25-day, 2,500 mile race. Its route covers the Alps, Pyrénéss, Massif Central, and Paris. Merckx won the Tour five times, and his achievements made him a national hero in Belgium.

He was first noticed on the cycling scene when he broke the unwritten rules and hurtled off during a race, leaving his team and leader behind. Then, he went on to win numerous one-day classic

Below *Eddy Merckx was five times winner of the grueling Tour de France – cycling's ultimate test.*

races, and although he was at his peak during 1971–2, he still beat all rivals.

But the French felt Meckx won more than was good for him – and with too much self-confidence; during the Tour de France, he was always greeted with catcalls at the finish of every stage. In 1975, at the end of an exhausting stage in the Pyrénées, at the top of a mountain pass he was attacked by a French spectator and hit so hard that he was forced to cling to the barrier for support. That same year, he missed a record-breaking sixth Tour win because of a collision during the final week. He broke a cheekbone and could not eat solid foods. But, against all medical advice, Merckx continued with the race and challenged right until the finish, so that the winner would gain a true victory and not a token win because of his withdrawal.

Merckx was forced to miss the 1976 Tour through illness, and the next year, his last Tour de France, he placed sixth.

Above *Eddy Merckx winning the 1974 Tour de France.*

1945	born in Belgium
1964	Amateur World Champion cyclist
1965	becomes a professional cyclist
1969	suspended during Tour of Italy on suspicion of illegal drug taking, acquitted and sabotage suspected
1969/70/71/72/74	wins Tour de France
1967/71/74	World Champion cyclist
1968/70/72/73/74	wins Tour of Italy
1978	retires and runs own bicycle factory

16
Gareth Edwards

South Wales is a notable breeding ground for rugby players, and one of the greatest to come from "the green valleys" is Gareth Edwards. He won his first rugby cap at the age of nineteen and a year later was the youngest ever captain of Wales.

Edwards was born in a small mining village. His father was a miner, and Edwards, whose family spoke Welsh at home, went to local schools until he won a scholarship to Millfield, a school famous for its sporting achievements. Although he trained as a teacher, he went to work in business for a company which was sympathetic to the demands that rugby made on his time.

Edwards played for Cardiff, where he was joined by Barry John, and together they formed the most successful halfback partnership in the

Below *Gareth Edwards, one of rugby's greatest scrum-halves, crashes over for another try.*

history of the game.

Although Edwards was a complete all-rounder, at scrum-half he was arguably the best player ever seen. He contributed to the revival of Welsh and British rugby in the early 1970s, and his performance for the British Lions in South Africa in 1974 set new standards for scrum-half play.

He played for Wales in a record number of 53 matches and also scored a record number of 20 tries. He was aggressive, athletic, and strong, and he developed a very long spin pass from his right hand. From a scrum or lineout near the opposition's line, he was especially dangerous because he could use his strength to power through their defences and score.

But Edwards was also a practical joker. During the 1968 Lions tour of South Africa, the infamous "Wreckers," as they were called, almost got the team sent home because of their childish behavior – pranks, bawdy songs, and beer drinking.

Edwards retired from world rugby in 1978 to work in business. He is now a well-known British television sports commentator.

Above *Gareth Edwards, on one of his dangerous runs, looks for someone to pass the ball to.*

1947	born in South Wales
1966	joins Cardiff Rugby Football Club
1967	first appearance for Wales, against France in Paris
1968	captain of Wales for first time against Scotland at Cardiff
1968	tours with British Lions to South Africa
1971	tours with Lions to New Zealand
1971	Wales wins Grand Slam and Triple Crown for first time since 1952
1974	tours with Lions to South Africa
1976	Wales wins Grand Slam and Triple Crown
1978	Wales wins Grand Slam and Triple Crown. Edwards retires, works in business and then as TV commentator

17

Olga Korbut

During the 1972 Munich Olympics, the first Games televised in prime time, the world was captivated by the dynamic personality, style, and fearlessness of a seventeen-year-old gymnast from the USSR.

Olga Korbut's 30-minute television debut turned her into a superstar, and her performance inspired millions of young girls to take up gymnastics.

During the 1972 Olympics, Korbut fell during her bars' routine and lost all hope of the combined gold medal, but the world still backed her because she had won the hearts of her audience. She was tiny; only 4'1" tall and weighing just under 85 pounds, and she displayed flamboyant originality with a cheery smile.

Two days after her fall, she was back on the bars, and the crowd halted the competition with

Below *The brilliant Russian gymnast performing on floor, bars, and beam.*

loud protests because they thought the judges' score was too low. Their noise made no difference to the results, but then Korbut went on to win two individual golds on beam and floor – with marks which some people in gymnastics thought were not strictly deserved.

A particularly flexible spine gave Korbut enormous physical range, and at Munich she performed her legendary backward somersault on the beam. Afterward, this exercise was almost banned by the International Gymanstics Federation, which considered it too dangerous, but they were forced to change their minds when Korbut threatened to retire.

Rumanian Nadia Comaneci joined Korbut in the international arena and took over as the world's most celebrated gymnast. She did not have Korbut's charisma, but at the Montreal Olympics, she was the first gymnast to score a perfect 10.00 points, and Korbut, taking part in her final competition, had to be satisfied with just one silver medal.

Above *Korbut's performance at the Montreal Olympics in 1972 thrilled audiences everywhere.*

1955	born in USSR
1964	joins local gymnastics club and is sent to special sports school
1969	enters Soviet National Championships
1972	Munich Olympics – wins 2 individual gold medals for beam and floor exercise, a silver medal for bars and a team gold medal
1973	European Championships at Wembley – loses to Tourischeva
1974	World Championships, Bulgaria – loses to Tourischeva
1976	Montreal Olympics, wins an individual silver on beam
1977	retires

18
Martina Navratilova

It is sometimes said that Martina Navratilova makes tennis boring because there are so few who can match her play on the court.

Until she finally won the US Open in 1983, she was called a "choker," someone who loses when it matters most. But in the past few years, she has emerged as an almost invincible player, accumulating strings of unbroken victories and a number one world ranking in tennis for the past five years.

Navratilova was born in Czechoslovakia. Her father committed suicide when she was young, and she was bought up by her mother and step-father, who encouraged her tennis and instilled in her the ultimate dream of one day winning the Wimbledon Ladies Championship.

By the age of ten, the skinny little girl was committed to the sport and took coaching lessons with George Parma, a former top Czech player. Success inevitably took her abroad, and at the

Above and right *Fitness, agility, power, and incredible determination have enabled Martina Navratilova to win more tennis championships than any other women player.*

age of eighteen, after a number of clashes with Czech tennis authorities, she decided to defect to the West.

When she first began playing for the US, Navratilova was not popular with the public. She believes in saying what she thinks and upset some people by admitting she was bisexual. She also says she dislikes the general American view that girls should cheer the boys on rather than play games themselves!

Navratilova always strives for maximum performance when she plays tennis and employs a number of people to advise on nutrition, psychology and footwork, as well as a regular playing coach. Her dedication works. In 1984, for example, she earned more money than all athletes in the world except three boxers. She won $2,173,556 – more than the men's record amount set in 1982!

Navratilova is settled in the West now. In 1986, she visited Czechoslovakia for the first time since she defected – playing for the US against her former country in the Federation Cup.

1956 born in Czechoslavakia
1975 defects to US and becomes US citizen in 1981
1978/79 and 1982–86 ranked world number one women's tennis player
1983/84/86 wins US Open championship
1978/79 and 1982–87 wins Wimbledon singles title
1984 makes 74 consecutive wins to beat Chris Evert Lloyd's 55
1984 wins Grand Slam and collects $1 million

19
Daley Thompson

The decathlon tests every aspect of the all-round athlete, and Daley Thompson, who has won every honor in the event, wants to prove he is the greatest all-rounder ever. Some might say he has already achieved that goal.

The decathlon is a grueling two-day event. On the first day, the athletes compete in the 100m, long jump, shot putt, high jump, and 400m. On the following day, they tackle the 110m high hurdles, discus, pole vault, javelin, and finally 1500m.

Thompson has won two Olympic gold medals in the event and is the only athlete ever to have held Commonwealth, European, World, and Olympic titles at the same time. He is a superb competitor and last lost a major decathlon in 1978. When the pressure is on, he delivers outstanding performances which beat all opposition. He is an entertainer, loved by the crowds, and has made the decathlon a popular event, putting it back into the main sports arena.

Below *Daley Thompson, the supreme all-round athelete, putting the shot, pole vaulting, and hurdling.*

He comes from London. His father, who died in 1971, was Nigerian, and his mother is Scottish. He was first sent to a private boarding school and later went to a local college in London.

As a boy, Thompson was keen on soccer and went for try-outs with Fulham and Chelsea league clubs. A professional soccer career looked certain, but in the summer of 1974, his headmaster sent him along to the nearby athletics club. His natural speed quickly brought him success at national level, but it was obvious he had wider talents. The following year, he competed in his first decathlon, and since then, has never looked back.

Thompson did not need to find a career. Athletes can now earn money from their sport – through sponsors, training grants, and prize and appearance money, and he trains relentlessly to a carefully planned daily schedule. This way, he can keep producing record scores and maintain his position as the world's number one decathlete.

Above *The long jump in the decathlon event at the 1984 Olympics.*

1958	born in England
1978/82/86	Commonwealth champion
1980/84	Olympic decathlon champion
1982/86	European champion
1983	World champion
1980	first sets world record for decathlon – holds it for 27 days
1982	May, regains world record, but loses it in August
1982	September, regains world record, at European Championships
1984	sets world record at Los Angeles Olympics

20
Jahangir Khan

Jahangir Khan's older brother died of a heart attack during a championship squash match. His death devasted the Khan family, and at the graveside, Khan vowed he would achieve what his brother had set out to do and become world champion.

As a child, Khan was small, weak, and sickly, and he was told he would never make it to the top. At the early age of seventeen, he was the world's number one squash player. By the time he reached twenty-two, Khan had been world champion five times and had won every major title in the game at least three times.

Khan has an impeccable squash pedigree and comes from a dynasty of champions dating back to the 1930s. But even though his father was world

Right *Jahangir Khan beats Geoff Hunt in 1981. He stayed undefeated as world champion for five and a half years.*

champion, the family was poor and lived in cramped conditions with no facilities in Karachi. Now, however, squash is big business, and the Khans are financially secure.

Most of the year, Khan lives with his cousin Rahmat and his family in England, where world-class squash facilities, competition, and tournaments are readily available. Rahmat gave up his own competitive career to coach Jahangir.

Khan is a devout Muslim. He is shy and retiring by nature, and his dedication to the game of squash is total. As a player, he is formidable: he is mentally and physically strong, and on court, fast, efficient and clinical. No champion is totally invincible forever, but it took five-and-a-half years and 500 matches before Khan was finally beaten – while playing for the world title in 1986.

Above *Jahangir practicing in Pakistan.*

1963	born in Pakistan
1979	wins World Amateur Squash Championships
1981	wins British Open final – loses to world champion Geoff Hunt, Khan's last defeat for five-and-a-half years
1981	November, defeats Hunt and becomes World Champion on the second anniversary of his brother's death
1983	beats Gamal Awad in longest match in squash history: 2hr 46min
1986	run of five world titles halted, beaten by Ross Norman of New Zealand

Glossary

Amateur Athletes who do not earn a living from their sports.

Bisexual To have sexual relations with both men and women.

Sporting arena The world of sport or a place where sports are played.

Century When a batsman scores one hundred runs in cricket.

Charisma A special personal quality or power which certain individuals have and which enables them to influence others.

Checkered flag The black and white checked flag shown to the finishers at the end of an auto race.

Circuit A series of events in one sport, for example, golf circuit, tennis circuit.

Defect To leave one's country of origin for another of opposing political views.

Grand National A major horse race over fences held at Aintree race course in England.

Grand Prix The title given to the most important motor car races.

High riding stroke A front crawl arm action in swimming.

Incorrigible Somebody whose behavior is beyond reform.

Line-out The method for restarting the game in rugby union, when the ball has gone out of bounds.

Over In cricket, a set of six or eight balls bowled by a bowler from one end of the pitch.

Pacifist A person who believes that one should not take part in war.

Pedigree The line of descent of a family.

Phenomenal Outstanding or remarkable.

Professional Athletes who earn a living from their sports – the opposite of amateur.

Racism Aggressive attitudes by members of one race toward another.

Rugby "cap" A special cap earned by a player when selected to play rugby for his country.

Slalom/giant slalom In skiing, when a contestant races against the clock and passes through various poles. Giant slalom is a ski race held on a long course, combining slalom and downhill.

Scrum In rugby, when the forwards on both sides pack together. This is a set scrummage or scrum; the scrum half from one team puts the ball into the scrum to restart play.

Spin pass A pass in rugby when the ball is spun to give greater speed and distance.

Sponsorship To provide financial support for sporting events, teams or individuals.

Steeplechase A horse race over two miles involving jumps over fences and ditches.

Time trials A competitive event in which unpaced cyclists are individually timed over a set distance.

Versatile Many-sided ability.

Further reading

Amazing but True Sports Stories by Phyllis and Zander Hollander (Scholastic, 1986)

Babe Ruth to Jackie Robinson by Naunerle C. Farr (Pendulum Press, 1979)

A Day at the Races by Harold Roth (Pantheon, 1983)

It's a Girl's Game Too by Alice Siegel (Henry Holt, 1980)

Killy! The Sports Career of Jean-Claude Killy by James and Lynn Hahn (Crestwood House, 1981)

Modern Soccer Superstars by Bill Gutman (Dodd, Mead, 1980)

Pele, the King of Soccer by Clare and Frank Gault (Dell, 1977)

Strange and Incredible Sports Happenings by Mac Davis (Putnam, 1982)

Superstars of Women's Track by George Sullivan (Dodd, Mead, 1981)

Winners Never Quit: Athletes Who Beat the Odds by Nathan Aaseng (Lerner, 1980)

Winners Under Twenty-One: America's Spectacular Young Sports Champions by Associated Features (Random House, 1982)

Index

Picture acknowledgements

Photographs supplied by All-Sport 15, 21, 23, 25, 27, 29, 31, 33, 35, 37, 39, 40, 43, 45; Topham Picture Library 7, 9, 10, 17; and Wayland 45.